Play your part!

How offshore workers can help improve health and safety

ISBN 0 7176 0786 0

Contents

. . . .

The Health and Safety Commission has endorsed
the practical guidance contained in this
document, which it commends to the industry.

Oil Industry Advisory Committee

Foreword

A C Barrell

Chief Executive
HSE Offshore
Safety Division
(OSD)

In his report on the Piper Alpha disaster, Lord Cullen recommended:

The regulatory body, operators and contractors should support and encourage the involvement of the offshore workforce in safety. In particular, first line supervisors should involve their workforce teams in everyday safety.

In response to this recommendation, the Health and Safety Commission's Oil Industry Advisory Committee (OIAC) set up a Working Group to review and suggest ways of improving the involvement of the offshore workforce in safety. This guidance is the result and thanks are due to all members of the Working Group who gave their time and experience to produce it. The guidance is intended to help operators, contractors, trade unions, safety representatives and individual employees to co-operate to improve health and safety offshore through the active participation of the workforce.

The guidance draws on many examples of good practice and success stories from the industry, involving the workforce in improving health and safety. We do not say that every operator must do everything exactly as set out in this guidance. But we hope it gives you a way of thinking about how well the workforce in your company is involved in health and safety; and some practical tips from the experience of others in your industry. At various points in the text we ask questions which we hope will prompt ideas and discussions at your workplace.

Offshore operations are carried out in isolated, remote locations and in an environment of continuous change: for example changes in activities, weather conditions, movements of vessels or helicopters. Typically, the employees of several different employers will be working closely together and need to co-operate with each other. All these factors add to the importance of continuing vigilance and positive planning, to establish and maintain good standards.

Above all, a strong health and safety culture means winning the hearts and minds of everybody working offshore.

Note:
Throughout this booklet, we use the terms 'workforce' and 'employee' to refer to everyone working offshore, whether an operator or a contractor.

Section 1

Why involving the workforce is important

....

Offshore safety involves everyone!

Making sure everything is done properly needs planning and co-operation.

The law sets the framework, by identifying key roles:

1. **Those responsible for offshore activities.** Installation **operators and owners** and other **employers** of staff who work offshore, have legal duties to ensure the health and safety of those who work offshore and all who are affected by their activities.

   In particular, on an offshore installation the operator or owner will set policy, provide the main resources for health and safety and co-ordinate management of the operation. Many other employers may have people working for them on the installation, or in connected activities such as diving. They too have legal duties to ensure the health and safety of offshore workers. They must co-operate with the operator or owners and each other, to ensure that activities can be managed safely.

   Line managers, down to front-line supervisors, who act on behalf of those with the primary duties, must understand their responsibilities to ensure safe working and be equipped to carry them out.

2. **Individual employees** have legal duties to take care of their own and others' safety and to co-operate with management in meeting their obligations. Everyone who works offshore must recognise this responsibility and act accordingly.

3. Offshore workers may elect **safety representatives** to speak to management for them on health and safety matters. Safety representatives have special training and some defined functions: for example, they can carry out inspections (with or without management), be involved in investigating incidents etc. They often act as a contact point for the workforce with HSE inspectors who visit the installation.

   In general, safety representatives help individual employees to keep in touch with important developments which may affect their health and safety, including the preparation of the installation 'safety case' (see Section 5).

   Safety committees which include safety representatives and management provide a regular forum for co-operation.

4. Companies have a responsibility to appoint competent **health and safety advisers**. Usually, though not always, these will be staff in the employer's Health, Safety and Environment Department. Advisers give expert support to management and can also inform and advise others - including safety representatives and employees - when they need it.

   Obviously some people will fill more than one of these roles, at any time. What is common to all of them is the need for competence and commitment to the principle that safe practice is an essential part of doing a job well.

Stop and think:
In what ways are you involved in health and safety?

Why is it important to involve the workforce?

.... Employees should be involved because:

they benefit from high standards of health and safety.

A man working for a sub-contractor broke his ankle after falling down some stairs on an oil rig. He was in a hurry and was carrying in both arms a 5 ft long steel bar weighing about 50 lbs. Although the stairs were well lit, they were slippery from a mixture of water and drilling mud. They were designed to be non-slip, but were curved at the front.

How does your company involve its workers in trying to prevent accidents like this? Think of both permanent matters like the design of the stairs and temporary ones like conditions underfoot and the task being done. Think of worksite inspections, hazard-spotting campaigns, tool-box talks, safety meetings etc. Also don't forget that the injured man worked for a sub-contractor, not the operator.

.... Employees should be involved because: they have the most direct contact with work hazards so should know what the problems are at first hand.

One operator found that their main accidents were slips, trips and falls, so they launched a special campaign with a video at safety meetings. Workers were then asked to complete checklists for their work areas. Over 400 were completed. These were all followed up and the operator will be looking at the future accident record to see how the situation improves.

.... Employees should be involved because:

they are more likely to stick to a health and safety plan if they have been involved in drawing it up.

On a hook-up contract, a man was lucky to escape death when he fell 30 ft through a hole in the drillfloor where the rotary table was going to be installed. Fortunately he only suffered minor injuries. The hole was covered by four loose scaffold boards and one slipped when he stood on it. The job had a permit, but the worksite was not inspected beforehand. It was up to supervisors to decide whether to inspect sites before issuing permits. A lot of permits could be issued on busy days, so they had to be selective. If they decided to look at a site first, they relied on their experience to spot hazards, as they did not have any special training.

How could the people involved have prevented this accident? Think particularly about how a proper safety plan, which includes rules for inspecting sites, pre-job talks, hazard-spotting routines, training and safe ways of working might have helped.

Could a simple but serious accident like this happen in your company - to you even? If not, what techniques for workforce involvement help you avoid it?

.... Employees should be involved because:

it will help to create a safety culture and a commitment to safety at all levels of the organisation.

One operator holds four meetings each year to bring together managers, safety advisers, safety representatives and contract workers from five different platforms. These meetings set and check health, safety and environmental objectives for the whole field as well as providing an informed forum to discuss key topics.

One contractor has regular safety steering meetings at which representatives from every live project meet senior onshore staff to exchange views and experiences, both good and bad, to build a safety culture.

How are you kept informed about safety issues in other parts of your company? Do you get to meet colleagues who you do not normally work with?

· · · · · · · · · · · ·   ·

.... Employees should be involved because:

Employers and others have duties under the Health and Safety at Work etc Act 1974 which they cannot meet without help from their workforce.

Many employers have already recognised the benefits. As one managing director explained:

"It is on the installations themselves where the best ideas will be generated, where the greatest achievements can be made and above all where the individual has a key role to play in the management of safety."

One company used its workforce to select escape and survival equipment. Samples of descenders, life-jackets and survival suits were sent offshore. Comments were fed back to the manufacturer until the offshore workers were happy with the products.

This is why involvement is so important. The following parts of this booklet show ways in which the workforce can participate.

Lord Cullen said the whole workforce must be committed to safe working practices. He picked out the safety representative and committee system as the most visible way of involving the workforce. Other ways include giving information, improving communication at all levels, good induction and training and making sure that people feel truly involved in the decisions affecting them.

Section 2

Building a good safety culture

Every group of people develops a 'culture' - shared attitudes, beliefs and ways of behaving. In an organisation with a good culture, everyone puts safety high on the list, which influences the ways in which group members handle new events and decisions. They know, for example, that they are not expected to react to a problem by cutting corners on safety for operational needs.

An effective culture needs to have good ways of informing and consulting the workforce. It helps to have a company policy which makes it clear that everyone has a role to play in improving health and safety and they must take part. Each operator or owner's written safety case must contain a statement of each company's policy and a description of the safety management system to deliver it. Some key issues are:

■ *the fact that everyone has a role to play, especially front-line supervisors*

■ *commitment by top management to involving the workforce*

■ *clear goals and ways to check they are met*

■ *effective two-way communications*

■ *consultation*

■ *co-operation between operator and contractor employees*

■ *training*

These can be grouped into the four 'C's of health and safety culture:

CONTROL

COMPETENCE

CO-OPERATION

COMMUNICATION

Section 3 looks at how these can help staff to implement the policy.

An existing company will already have a safety culture, but may want to strengthen it. A new policy for involving the workforce will probably be needed. It might help to get an idea of the attitudes of the workforce now and to identify past successes and failures. For example:

One drilling contractor asked its employees, safety representatives and Offshore Installations Managers (OIMs) how well the safety representative system was working and if it could be improved. It found that two out of three safety representatives wanted more training in workplace safety.

Management need to show commitment by example and in everyday decisions.

What do you think about your company's safety culture?

What is your company's policy on how it involves its workforce?

Is this policy up-to-date or in need of an overhaul?

Do you know why your company involves its workforce in the way it does - what does it hope to get out of the process?

Section 3

How the workforce can be involved

How can a company involve the workforce? This is how one approached it:

"A key factor ... is explicit agreement of responsibilities. With this company, the process started at the top. Every single activity was discussed and responsibilities were assigned by the President of the company. Responsibility for several activities, mainly those related to policy issues, remained with the President, who considered these part of his primary responsibility. For each of the remaining activities, he indicated who in the management chain was responsible. As the process continued, cascading through the organisation, we agreed relevant primary responsibility with each manager and supervisor.

"For each individual, the process clarifies responsibility for identified activities, as assigned by his or her manager or supervisor. This ensured that safety and health responsibilities were truly integrated with line management roles."

Control

An effective management system needs control. People need to be clearly told what they are responsible for and how their duties will be checked.

One operator has integrated safety fully into group and individual work objectives and has given every supervisor this main safety objective:

"Overall responsibility to ensure that all company and contract personnel in the ... field are aware of the company commitment to safety as first priority of corporate policy and direct personnel towards compliance."

The supervisor was given two personal targets, one a personal safety task, the other a duty to involve staff:

1 *to complete at least six site safety inspections by the end of the year; and*

2 *to attend at least two safety meetings with all subordinates by the end of the year.*

Competence

As well as the competence needed for their work tasks, which obviously include health and safety issues, employees need to be competent for any specific safety role, eg it would be unfair and pointless getting supervisors to do safety inspections or run meetings unless they are also given the skills to do them well. Many people - managers, supervisors and safety representatives - need to be trained in how to make presentations, negotiate, run meetings etc if a culture of real workforce participation is going to be a success.

One company has started a major initiative in training safety representatives through its Safety Representatives Development Programme. The programme has clearly defined aims to:

1 *develop jointly with management, HSE and advisers, the role of the safety representatives individually and as a group, promote and improve the health and safety of the whole workforce and improve the efficiency and effectiveness of operations;*

2 *agree and implement a common approach to improving safety performance, including an action plan to be jointly developed and supported by the safety representatives and management;*

3 *enable safety representatives to begin to identify and develop skills to help them fulfil their role more effectively.*

The programme is divided into four stages:

Stage 1 Pre-workshop work

To bring course participants to a common level of understanding.

Stage 2 Residential workshop

To develop a joint action plan with management to implement improvements.

Stage 3 Development of the action plan

To follow up and implement the action plan.

Stage 4 Evaluation

Review workshops to evaluate progress and develop further joint actions and plans.

TRAINING

One way to identify people's training needs is by job and task analysis. This should include:

■ getting information from employees about how jobs are done, the sequence of tasks and the tools, materials and equipment used;

■ watching and asking people, to understand what they are doing and why;

■ asking them what extra training they think they need.

The tasks should include each part of a person's job. It would be easy to concentrate on technical training and forget tasks like how to run a safety seminar.

How good is your company's way of finding out people's training needs?

Does it include non-technical skills?

Are employees consulted?

Here is one operator's approach set out in a statement. It is quite structured and you can see that their employees are closely involved in it.

"None of us can fulfil our responsibilities and do our jobs properly unless we know what to do and how to do it. Training is part of the process of developing the right knowledge and skills so that we are equipped to perform well. We should identify who needs training, provide it and check its effectiveness.

"Our goals are to ensure that:

■ *responsibilities for identifying and defining training needs and initiating training are clearly established;*

■ *criteria are established for the specialised safety and environmental training of all personnel according to job, experience and certification requirements. Criteria include subject matter, learning objectives, training content, length and location, refresher training etc;*

■ *particular training is provided as follows:*

- *standard safety and environmental training for facility supervisors;*

- *hazard identification and assessment training for selected management, operations, drilling and technical workers;*

- *appropriate refresher training.*

■ *the effectiveness of training in critical tasks is monitored and assessed, eg by observing behaviour and testing knowledge to ensure the person can perform the task correctly."*

Finally, it is sensible to check how useful training has been. Has it met the need? One golden rule - ask the pupil. This is one operator's approach:

"Training is evaluated for effectiveness and necessary improvements made. Was it timely and appropriate? Did it meet the learning objectives? Has it produced the right job performance? Evaluations should be performed by the trainee, together with his or her supervisor."

Another operator said:

"For many newly-elected safety representatives, this is the first time that they have been in the classroom since leaving school. Almost without exception, the courses have been well received. Many of the benefits were not directly related to the course content but were more about the companionship and teamwork which develops outside the course.

"Safety representatives have spoken of the value of 'after-hours sessions' - these include sharing common problems and learning how these have been tackled on other installations.

"All of this increases the safety representatives' confidence in dealing with their constituents and supervisors and these cross-platform contacts are often maintained after the courses have finished."

Co-operation

Co-operation is particularly important on an offshore installation because of the many different work groups present. In a close community as exists offshore, it should not be too difficult to achieve. One way of encouraging it is to set up teams to look at specific problems. Here are some examples:

One company set up a group of 40 employees, led by the safety officer, to look at people's needs for protective equipment. They carried out trials and recommended what should be bought. They looked first at hearing and eye protection, then went on to consider coveralls and safety footwear.

Another group, from different platforms and companies, worked together to solve the problem of noisy accommodation. The operator carried out their recommendations.

In one company, the Permit-to-Work-System (PTW) is used for basic worksite risk assessment on offshore installations. If a task is particularly complex, or involves a number of disciplines or has an accident/incident history, it may be necessary to carry out a more rigorous hazard assessment using a Job Safety Analysis (JSA). This involves a meeting of all workers within the work area, chaired by an appropriate senior person. Each step of the task is systematically considered for potential hazards and suitable precautions agreed by the group. The results of the JSA are recorded on a JSA form and a copy of this is attached to the PTW form.

How does your company get its workers to co-operate with each other on health and safety problems?

Communication

Good communication is essential. Information should go up, down and across the organisation in a way that suits the people receiving it.

Some examples of written communications are:

- safety bulletins addressed to a particular group of employees;

- handbooks with technical information and control measures;

- minutes of safety meetings.

This is one operator's communication system:

"Our goals are to ensure that:

- *each new starter is made fully familiar with the workplace, his or her job and the safety requirements. Supervisors guide new starters on what is expected of them, any hazards they may face and provide the necessary specific safety information to ensure they don't put themselves or others at risk. The supervisor should document their orientation process;*

- *regular person to person contacts are made between supervisors and their staff to communicate safety-related issues. Communication should be open, two-way and aim to cement effective working relationships;*

- *important safety-related information, correspondence and news are effectively communicated. Such information may include lessons learned from incidents, Loss Prevention Bulletins, notices posted by management or supervisors etc. Means of communication may include individual distribution, display on bulletin boards, or discussion at work group meetings."*

Another company stresses the need for open communications, eg:

- *feedback from the last project at the induction for the next;*

- *anonymous questionnaires about various aspects of how the operations are run;*

- *policy steering committees for safety representatives both offshore and onshore;*

- *onshore conferences with brainstorming sessions for supervisors;*

- *safety quiz competitions for employees as part of welfare activities.*

An operator in the southern sector has helped safety representatives on several different platforms to set up a successful quarterly newsletter, by circulating it for them.

HSE has set up a wider circulation of the OIAC newsletter *Health and safety news for the oil industry* to ensure that it goes to all safety committees. It contains information about current issues in the oil and gas industry (both onshore and offshore). The format and layout have been changed to make it more readable and the wider circulation should ensure that it reaches most of the workforce offshore.

Safety meetings can be a good way of getting information across and seeking ideas. The law requires safety committees to meet at least once every three months. Some companies find it worth meeting more often. There are many other kinds of meetings as well. Here is a trade union's view of a useful pattern:

- *Platform safety committee - one every month or six weeks to get different views;*

- *General safety meeting - one per trip, chaired by a safety officer;*

- *Safety meeting - weekly for a specific work group squad, chaired by the safety representative and minutes taken by the supervisor;*

- *Tool box talk - daily, or for each new task, with the supervisor;*

- *Offshore induction - for new employees on each platform;*

- *Onshore induction - for new employees.*

*How does your company
communicate with you?*

Is it two-way?

Safety meetings must be well run.
For example, meetings benefit from:

■ clear objectives;

■ the right people attending
(those who can contribute and make decisions);

■ chairing and participation skills
(training can help);

■ good time management, so that the meeting
finishes its business and concentrates on
what is important;

■ careful minuting and timely follow-up,
where necessary;

■ feedback to others.

*Above all meetings should
not be boring! Videos and
presentations can help. It
can also be useful for
members of the workforce
to use meetings to describe
their own experiences.*

Section 4

Setting and maintaining standards .....

Developing a culture and a policy is a good way to start. However, to make sure everything goes ahead as planned, standards and detailed targets need to be set. For example:

One operator's policy goal is to "continuously improve safety protection". To make the goal a reality, they put it in their annual business plan, with objectives set for named people, with deadlines - ie clear measurable goals. One goal is to introduce and develop a system of recognition for good safety performance.

Another company sets out in writing the aims of meetings. Conditions are laid down on how often meetings should be held, how to record views and decisions and feedback. Performance measures are set to check if the meetings have actually worked. They include simple matters like have the meetings been held often enough and did everyone go, as well as checking to see that agreed actions were carried out! And last but not least, ensuring proper feedback to people who raised problems.

Here is a simple example to show the difference between a vague objective that will probably not be much use and a target that can be seen and checked:

A manager could be made responsible for ensuring that his or her department "has an effective means of consulting employees on health and safety matters, including a committee which will meet regularly and report to the Director of Safety".

This is open to different interpretations and difficult to monitor. It could however, be:

"to have an effective means of consulting employees on health and safety matters, including a safety committee which will meet once a quarter, circulate agreed minutes within two weeks of each meeting and submit an action plan for correcting problems noted, with the minutes, to the Director of Safety".

The difference is that the second option is measurable. Everyone knows what is wanted. In other words 'what gets measured gets done'. The targets set out at the beginning of this section are one way of measuring what happens.

Senior managers should ask:

■ are performance standards set?

■ are they right and realistic?

■ are they being met?

■ are they helping us to do what we planned?

■ what is our record on accidents, ill health and incidents?

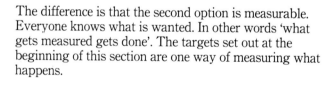

How are you involved in setting and reviewing performance measures?

It is important that employees have a say in agreeing the measures, checking they are met and seeing what lessons can be learned from them. There is no point in a company deciding what it wants from involving its workforce, how to get it and measure it, unless it is able to learn the lessons. This includes auditing - collecting information on how well each part of safety management is being done and drawing up action plans. To audit effectively, a company should have a way of reviewing and revising its policy on encouraging the workforce to participate in health and safety.

Section 5

The safety case ......

What is a safety case?

A safety case is a **written document** prepared by the **operator** of a fixed installation or **owner** of a mobile installation. It sets out comprehensive information on arrangements for **managing health and safety** and **controlling major accident hazards** on the installation.

The safety case must show that:

■ the management system adequately covers all statutory health and safety requirements;

■ there are proper arrangements for an independent audit of the system;

■ the risks of major accidents have been identified and assessed;

■ measures to reduce risks to people to the lowest reasonable level have been taken;

■ proper systems for emergency arrangements on evacuation, escape and rescue are in place.

A safety case must be submitted to HSE for acceptance. This will be a written confirmation that HSE is satisfied with the case for health and safety made out in the document. The safety case will be revised and updated whenever needed throughout the life cycle of the installation.

How is the workforce involved?

A guide to the Offshore Installations (Safety Case) Regulations 1992: guidance on Regulations (ISBN 011 882055 9, available from HSE Books) emphasises the importance of the variety of arrangements that operators and owners need and want to make, to ensure that the whole workforce is actively involved in and committed to safe working practices. This section shows examples of approaches which have been successful.

The Regulations also say that safety representatives must be consulted on the preparation of the safety case. The safety case guidance gives examples of particular subjects which could be usefully covered. For example:

■ general health and safety policy;

■ risk analyses and proposed control measures;

■ important elements of the Safety Management System (SMS), such as training and PTW systems, arrangements for temporary refuge and the evacuation, escape and rescue analysis.

Safety representatives must also have access to the safety case contents. In particular, they:

■ have access to the complete document; and

■ are entitled to a written summary and may take copies of extracts, where needed, to carry out their representative role.

Involving the workforce -examples of company actions

One company treats workforce involvement in the safety case in the same way as workforce participation in weekly platform safety meetings, quarterly management safety reviews and accident investigations.

Involvement is in a number of ways:

- Information gathering - on older platforms, information from 'older hands' proves invaluable in understanding why plant is operated in a particular way;

- Hazard identification and control - benefits of 'hands on' experience. Workers are routinely involved in HAZOPs and WHAT-IF studies, eg a drilling crew considered the consequences of a dropped drill collar, based on an idea from a safety representative;

- Review of safety case studies - draft reports are provided to workers with relevant expertise for review and comment. Team reviews in scheduled working hours are carried out for the safety case;

- Open comment - after team reviews, copies are distributed to onshore and platform work groups for review and comment;

- 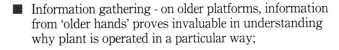 Workforce presentations - every member of the workforce is given the opportunity to attend a presentation on the safety case.

Benefits include improved awareness and recognition of installation hazards, better understanding of the hazard assessment process and a clearer idea of the ways in which safety is managed offshore.

What is HSE's role?

The operator or owner is responsible for the safety case and for controlling risks offshore. HSE decides whether an adequate case has been made for safe operation; the detail will be taken into account in later inspection plans.

During the assessment of a safety case, discussion and review between HSE inspectors and companies will often result in agreement on improvements needed and on timescales. If an urgent problem is found, HSE will want immediate action. If agreement is not possible, and a safety case is rejected, the company can ask for HSE's Executive (the Director-General and his two deputies) to review the decision.

As part of their normal inspection work, HSE inspectors meet safety representatives to tell them the purpose of the visit and the results of the inspection. Inspectors may also visit an installation to discuss any exemptions to legislation applied for by the operator: the safety representatives' views are taken into account when making decisions about exemptions, although this is only one of the many factors which have to be considered.

Similarly, the assessment of safety cases considers how much safety representatives have been involved. Installation safety representatives are invited to participate in any review by the Executive of a rejected safety case.

Section 6

A case study: how you can help prevent an accident .....

A man was seriously injured while replacing a valve in a high pressure line.

The accident happened when workers on one shift isolated the valve by shutting a valve on either side and opening the drain-line between. They knew the isolating valves were not operating properly so they closed the drain-line again. They left a message for the next shift that it must be reopened first to blow the line down. The PTW and Isolation Certificate did not describe the method of isolation in detail.

During the shift handover, the message was not passed on. A fitter (who was unfamiliar with that type of job) removed the clamp bolts holding the pipe flanges together, instead of just loosening them and cracking a joint. Pressure had built up in the line again and a coupling blew apart. The fitter received very serious head injuries and will never fully recover.

Having read through this guidance, think about how ways of involving the workforce in your company would help you avoid a similar incident. Here are some key points:

. . . .

1   *Responsibility for planning and checking the job;*

2   *Pre-task safety briefings;*

3   *The way of isolating the valve;*

4   *Checking and proving the isolation;*

5   *Role of PTW and other written procedures;*

6   *Shift handover arrangements;*

7   *Competence of everyone involved in the job;*

8   *Learning the lessons for the future from incidents and near-misses that do happen.*

Printed and published by the Health and Safety Executive   C300   6/94